pocket *hot*
super/sex

pocket *hot*
super/sex

tracey cox

London, New York, Munich, Melbourne, Delhi

Design XAB Design
Editor Becky Alexander
Senior Art Editor Helen Spencer
Senior Editor Peter Jones
Production Editor Luca Frassinetti
Production Controller Hema Gohil
Managing Editor Adèle Hayward
Category Publisher Stephanie Jackson
Art Director Peter Luff

First published in Great Britain in 2008
by Dorling Kindersley Limited,
80 Strand, London WC2R ORL

A Penguin Company

2 4 6 8 10 9 7 5 3 1

A CIP catalogue record for this book is
available from the British Library.

ISBN 978-1-4053-3267-5

Printed and bound in Singapore
by Star Standard
See our complete catalogue at **www.dk.com**

Contents

Introduction

This is my fifth pocket-size book, so it seems you enjoy reading the handy little pint-size versions as much as I enjoy putting them together for you! The idea of downsizing the big books is to add spice and life to weekends away, holidays abroad, and outside erotic adventures – without you having to lug around a bigger, heavier book. I've chosen sections of the original that are particularly applicable to these situations, but you'll find lots of other stuff crammed in here to send you into supersexy, sensory overdrive!

superhotsex is, as the title sounds, a raunchier, x-rated version of *supersex* and it's designed to gently, but firmly, prod you out of your comfort zone. Thing is, for most of us, sex isn't a problem at the start of a relationship. Everything is new, you're both out to please, and pleasure is delivered daily by the bucketload. Five years on, instead of devouring each other, you're devouring the latest bestseller. You're content, happy even, but you can't help but think… *what the hell happened to my sex life?*

Those of you who've read *supersex* know the basics and have no doubt mastered more than a few techniques. This book is designed to take your sex life to another level by getting you to be much more sexually adventurous. Yes, you might have to make a bit of an effort, but by God, it's going to be worth it!

Want more or better sex? (And doesn't everyone?) This little book might deliver more than you're expecting…

Tracey X

1 Sharing sexy stuff

How to get a fantasy from your head, into your bed.

We'd rather die than try some fantasies in reality. But others… well, you might not want to replicate them exactly, but you'd sure as hell like to capture the tummy-aching, skin-tingling, vagina-moistening, penis-lifting effect it has on your libido! Role-playing fantasies are one way to get the kick – without any of the malevolent misfires sometimes got by taking them through to real life. Here, you'll find tips, hints, and example scenarios to help you turn erotic thoughts into sexy, real-life escapades.

ROLE-PLAY RULES

As with every game, following a few basic guidelines will make everything run more smoothly:

- **It doesn't have to be literal:** symbolism is often all that's needed. For example, got a threesome fantasy? Adding a vibrator as the third person can give a sense of having two men doing different things simultaneously.
- **Expensive props** aren't necessary but the more effort you make, the better it usually is. Use music and different rooms of your home to suit different scenarios.

- **Try to choose fantasies** that appeal to both of you, particularly the first time round.
- **Work out the scenario together** beforehand: often that's just as much a turn-on as acting it out.
- **Be specific about** how "in character" you want each other to be – for some people, slipping back into your usual selves even for a minute, destroys the illusion.
- **Choose your time** and place to re-enact the fantasy: no flatmates, dogs wanting walkies, children wanting to know where their Batman suit disappeared to.

Sex play is like any other game – except there are no losers. **You both win with bigger, better, raunchier orgasms!**

- **Don't worry if you laugh** – just keep going. Lust will usually overtake the laughter once you start getting into it.
- **Work out an agreed "stop now" signal** because you might not like it as much as you thought! Make your "stop" word something that isn't ever going to be used as part of the roleplay. "Purple" is better than "more" for obvious reasons.
- **Don't be scared** to start the fantasy in public. Some – like "sex with a stranger" – lend themselves to the two of you meeting up in a bar before the real action starts. So long as you're not dressed weirdly or act abnormally, no-one need never know.

Let the games begin...

These are two popular fantasies already thought through for you. Feel free to add your own twists and surprises along the way…

THE FANTASY: *Deflowering a "virgin"*

Why it appeals: It's a power game with both submissive and dominant roles, each with its pluses. Men particularly like playing the virgin, after a lifetime of being the sexual persuader.

What you'll need: If she's doing the seducing, a "sexy secretary" outfit works well: a long pencil skirt, shirt unbuttoned to show off a push-up bra, stockings, high-heels. Think Mrs Robinson.

> **Fantasies** are just the thing to **transform you** from a tired commuter or worn-out parent to **sultry sex god**.

The action plan (her seducing him):

- Get both of you a drink, then take him into the living room. He sits on the sofa, you sit opposite, crossing your legs and hiking your skirt up. He's not sure where to look.
- Make chit-chat to suit the scenario (he's your friend's son who's dropped in to mow the lawn or the shy grocery delivery boy), then make it saucier. Tell him you don't think your husband finds you attractive. Does he think you're attractive? What bits? Why? Let him squirm as he tries to be politically correct – and hide the erection which is starting to happen. At which point you say…
- "You're looking a little uncomfortable. Let me help you". And you move from the chair to sit beside him on the sofa.

- You loosen the first two buttons of his shirt, telling him he looks hot and bothered. Rub your hand against his exposed chest saying, "Such soft skin. So unlike my husband's…"

Our **moods** and **desires** change constantly. Don't assume that the **scenario** that worked last night will put a **twinkle in his eye** the next day.

- As he squirms, you undo the top few buttons of your shirt, take his hand, and place it on the underside of your breast. Ask him how it feels and if he likes it. Keep making small talk. Ask him if he's ever made love to a woman before. He'll squeak out, "No". Ask him if he'd like to make love to you… It's OK, you won't tell and no-one's going to walk in.
- Ask him to take off your top and your bra. Tell him to touch your breasts and instruct him on how to do it. Moan and sigh, but you're still the grown-up so don't get too out of control.
- Ask him to stand up in front of you, unzip his trousers, and take out his (by now) throbbing penis. Admire it, say how hard it is compared to men your age, then give him exquisitely tortuous oral sex – stopping just short of orgasm. The idea is to bring him to a tantalising peak but not to the point of ejaculatory inevitability.
- Undress yourself – theatrically and maintaining eye contact throughout. Let his eyes caress your body but don't let him touch you. Leave on your high heels, stockings, and suspenders. Pose provocatively and caress your curves. Ask him if he likes what he sees and if he wants to touch you.

- Undress him, then lead him to the bed and promise to explain how to make love to a woman to make her scream. Honour the promise. Each touch, kiss, fondle, thrust is his very first, remember. At first he touches reverently, then he's lost in a frenzy of passion.
- The fantasy ends when he loses control completely – which he will in about three minutes if you've played your part properly!

Control and the **amount of power** the person has in **real life** often **dictates how much** they want in their **fantasy life**.

THE FANTASY: The sex slave

Why it appeals: Having complete sexual command has obvious benefits. You don't have to worry about the "no, you first" niceties of sex: it's all about YOUR pleasure. Meanwhile, the "slave" is "forced" to perform acts they'd secretly love to, but wouldn't dare suggest.

What you'll need to act it out: For this example, she's the slave and he's the master. Jeans and a leather jacket, undone over a naked chest, sets the scene nicely. You'll also need a blindfold, scarves to tie her up, and a wooden spoon or hairbrush. She's completely naked – helpless and vulnerable (just how you want her!).

The action plan (him seducing her):
- Try to keep an expressionless face. Don't say, "Are you OK?", "Did I hurt you?", "Are you sure you're enjoying this?" This isn't about her, it's all about you!!! You're the master, she's the slave!
- Start by ordering her to do small tasks – get you a drink, fluff up the pillows, give you a massage.

- Don't ask, order. Make it clear you are the boss and she is not to misbehave or she'll be punished (spank her with the wooden spoon or back of the hairbrush).
- Once you're both nicely in character, order her to sit or lie down, face turned away from you, blindfold her and tie her hands behind her back. Push her forward into a submissive position. She's now naked, bound, and blindfolded – completely at your mercy!
- Grab your wooden spoon or brush and administer a few short, sharp whacks on her bottom – even better if she begs you to stop.
- Start caressing her. Reach in between her legs – wait until she's moaning for more then… stop.

Blindfolds mean your partner can feel you, but not see what's happening. **Each touch is loaded with anticipation and surprise**.

- Tell her you decide what she gets and when – and she has to satisfy you first.
- Turn her around and order her to pleasure you. She can use her mouth; untie her hands if you want but keep the blindfold on.
- No matter how pleasurable, punctuate her stimulation of you by pushing her away when she seems to be enjoying herself the most. Tell her she's been a bad girl.
- Tease her: start to give her oral sex, then stop. Push your fingers inside her and when she starts thrusting against them, stop.
- The fantasy ends by you announcing (dramatically) that she's now free from her slavery – to service you.

Guilty pleasures
(Seriously, do you think I'm weird for thinking that?)

Now here's a comforting thought: no-one has worked out how to read minds yet. Which means it doesn't really matter what filthy thoughts are floating around in there!

If you choose, no-one but you need know about your fantasies. If they bring you pleasure, cause no-one else pain and worry you simply because they're a little politically incorrect or "weird", my advice would be to give yourself permission to go for it! Still concerned? Then keep reading…

What if I don't like a fantasy and want it to stop?

Our fantasies, like the rest of our lives, are influenced heavily by what's happened to us. It's a lucky person who sails through without negative experiences and these creep into our sexual scripts. Often, simply understanding where an urge comes from can stop you worrying. (An upsetting spanking at school might cause you to fantasize about it later, for instance.)

If the remorse and confusion post-fantasy outweighs the pleasure you get during it, you can actively banish it. If you're masturbating and the fantasy pops into your head, stop and consciously think of

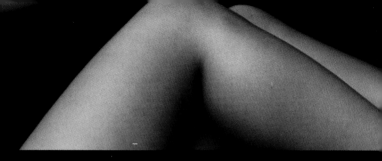

something else that doesn't cause you angst. Replace old fantasies with new ones by masturbating while reading and watching erotica. During sex, focus on the here and now: how your lover's touch feels. It's like breaking any other habit – you need to retrain your brain. Keep at it for a while and it should naturally slip away. If it doesn't and you're still worried, consider seeking professional help.

Am I weird if my fantasy is weird?

We'll often fantasize about things contrary to our core personality (Ms Goody Two-Shoes becomes the star of a particularly dirty orgy) simply because they revolve around something we wouldn't dare do in real life. There is no evidence at all to support that simply fantasizing about something leads you to act on it. Deviant fantasies can be an indicator of true sexual deviancy but it's invariably coupled with real-life symptoms as well. So long as you can distinguish between fantasy and reality, it's not a fixation (see overleaf), and you've got no desire to take it through to real life, there isn't usually a problem.

What if I don't have fantasies?

Some people are great cooks, others can't quite get the hang of the toaster. Same deal here. Creative people conjure up vivid

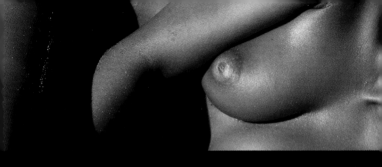

technicolour fantasies with intricate plot twists, scene changes, and mood-lighting tweaks. Others have problems imagining themselves walking across a room. If you're the latter, try focusing on your favourite erotic scene from a film or book, then individualize it. Put yourself in the lead role. See "Use your imagination" (opposite) for inspiration and, remember, a fantasy can be one simple image.

It's also not compulsory to have fantasies, by the way. If it doesn't do much for you, so be it. Some people adore planning a holiday, others buy tickets last minute, turn up, and see where it takes them. There's no right or wrong way.

What if I fantasize too much?

It's a bit like asking if you masturbate too much. Assuming you're not interrupting an important meeting to relieve yourself in the washroom, there is no such thing. If your fantasies aren't hurting anyone and you just have an active imagination, imagine away! Fantasizing keeps you on sexual simmer, which means your libido is alive and ready for action. But if you only get aroused and orgasm by focusing on one particular fantasy, or if your partner complains of you always being detached during sex, you may need professional advice

Finish the fantasy...

You've booked into a posh hotel and discover it offers erotic films on the television. This makes you feel decidedly sexy, so you book a massage. You have a bath and put on a robe over your naked body, when there's a knock at the door. You forget the film is playing and as the man is setting up the table, you see him stealing glances at the screen. You lie down and he says, "Exactly what sort of massage would you like?"...

You're in an empty carriage on a train. An attractive girl gets on and sits opposite you. She smiles but doesn't speak, just pulls out a book that, judging by the cover, is an erotic novel. As she reads, she steals glances at you, then rearranges herself so her skirt hikes up. She sees you watching and deliberately exposes more flesh. You take a chance, and put a tentative hand on the inside of her knee. She parts her legs, giving you permission to proceed...

Some other fantasy scenarios to inspire you:
• Boss and secretary
• Burglar surprises sleeping beauty
• Biker gang "forces" innocent girl into doing naughty things
• Cheerleader and football team
• Firefighter rescues very grateful victim
• Doctor and nurse
• Rock star and groupie
• Teacher with student

Porn vs plot

Here's something that will surprise you (not): men's fantasies tend to resemble porn films – instant action, close-ups of bits sliding into bits, graphic detail, and a focus on the physical.

Men also tend to fantasize about women they've got a chance with in real life. Their leading ladies are approachable, girl-next-door types (though the odd celeb begging to be taken does pop up – or down, as the case may be). They're aware the chance of happening upon a neighbour sunbathing topless is a tad more likely than a naked Jessica Alba popping by. The higher the chance of real-life probability, the more it arouses them. Whereas women, on the other hand, have no problems picturing George Clooney slipping his hand up their skirt.

Women's fantasies are based more around a plot situation: they set the scene (hunky tradesman comes to door etc.), then move onto specific sexual treats (oral sex featuring heavily). There's more conversation in women's fantasies as the narrative unfolds, whereas men tend to pepper theirs with grunts and groans of "oh baby".

Men say they think about things they've experienced, whereas women fantasize mainly about things they have never done. It's no surprise that men fantasize more when they're not getting it, but what is interesting is that women do the opposite. We're more likely to fantasize when we're having loads of good sex regularly. This supports a theory about female sexualiy: without stimulation, our libido retreats into a slumber. Use it or lose it – literally.

The top 20 male fantasies

- **Fantasies** about previous or anticipatory sex with a current partner.
- **A threesome** – usually watching two women having sex, then joining in. Great if it's sisters, heaven-sent if it's twins.
- **Sex with a woman** other than your partner (the ultimate: sex with a celebrity in front of your friends).
- **Anonymous,** spontaneous sex with a stranger.
- **Group sex** with a multitude of gorgeous women queuing to give you oral sex.
- **Unending oral sex** dispensed by just about every female you come into contact with.
- **Anal** sex.
- **Secretly** watching a woman undress and masturbate.
- **Sex in a public** or risky place.
- **Being seduced** by an older woman.
- **Seducing** a virgin.
- **Spying** on two other people having sex.
- **Having sex** with your mate's girlfriend.
- **S&M** – being tied up and spanked or whipped.
- **Sex with forbidden people** – your girlfriend's mother, your boss.
- **Sex** with a sex worker.
- **Watching** your partner be taken by another man.
- **Sex** with another man.
- **Being watched** and applauded for your sexual expertise.
- **A "pretend"** rape scenario.

The top 20 female fantasies

- **Fantasies** about previous or anticipatory sex with a current partner.
- **Sex with a man other than your partner** – seducing a friend or friend's partner is a favourite.
- **Sex** with a woman.
- **Sex** with someone at work.
- **A threesome** with two men, both fighting over your glorious body.
- **Sex** with a celebrity.
- **Being given expert oral sex** – under the desk at work, under the table at a restaurant.
- **Sex with a stranger** – with a penchant for tradesmen when you're home alone.
- **Being found irresistible** – a line of male supermodels, especially the ones in the Calvin Klein ads, jostling to get to you.
- **Being a sex worker** – the ultimate "nice girl" sin.
- **Romantic fantasies** – hot sex on a white, sandy beach.
- **Being deflowered** as a sacrificial virgin.
- **Being watched** with the voyeur desperate to have sex with you.
- **Being forced to strip** in front of a crowd of men.
- **Playing Mrs Robinson** and deflowering a male virgin.
- **Having an army** of physically perfect men as sex slaves.
- **Being "forced"** to have sex.
- **Starring in a porn film** – being lusted over worldwide.
- **Being seduced** by an authority figure.
- **S&M** – being tied up and spanked or whipped.

2 **Sex and the great outdoors**

How to make love in public without getting arrested.

The fear of discovery, pounding heartbeats, that delicious jolt of adrenalin when you think someone's coming (and it's not either of you two). Anyone who's ever had sex outside knows just how hot it can be. There's just one teensy problem: it's illegal to have sex in public. Happily, this is only a problem if you get caught and reported. There is a way to indulge alfresco and keep out of jail: it's called being sensible. Assess each situation carefully, stay fully clothed and use props to hide behind. A beach umbrella, sarong, or picnic blanket disguise a multitude of naughty acts; if you're really shy, a tent provides the privacy you need but still *feels* as though you're on show. Breathe some fresh air into your love life by giving one (or all) of the following a whirl.

ON OR IN THE CAR
How you do it: Yes, you could slip into the back seat and enjoy relative privacy but it's far, far, far sexier to do it on the car bonnet. She sits on the bonnet and he stands in front of her. She then wraps her legs around his waist to let him penetrate, then leans back, balancing herself with her arms. One word of caution though,

before you eagerly jump on board: the bonnet is made of metal. If you've been parked for a while and it's winter, it'll turn your cheeks to ice. Warm up the engine or put a coat down to lean back on. If it's a hot day, test the temperature first before you get burnt!

Why you'd risk it: It's über-erotic because not only do you risk getting caught, it's the sort of thing teenagers get up to. You both recapture the heady thrill of being an adolescent, feeling wild, free, and very *un*grown-up.

Chances of getting caught: Choose a suitably quiet street or country lane and the chances are low. Besides, you've got your get out right there. If a car appears from nowhere, both drop down and pretend to be examining a puncture.

Sex in a tent is legal because you're not in public view, but having sex while **others walk past** feels wonderfully wicked.

UP AGAINST A TREE

How you do it: She leans with her back against a (big, sturdy) tree. He stands in front of her. She then jumps up and wraps her legs around his waist and puts her arms around his neck, keeping her back firmly pressed against the tree for support. If there are any conveniently placed branches that look strong enough, try hanging onto those as well – it can make it a little easier. If that all sounds far too energetic, cheat by wrapping one leg around his waist and keeping the other on the floor for support. He should hold onto her thigh(s) no matter which position you choose.

Why you'd risk it: Because most of her weight is bearing down on his penis and her vagina is angled, penetration is deep, snug, and tight. If she squeezes her thigh muscles, she'll narrow the vaginal canal even further to give him the extra friction he needs to orgasm. It's raw sex at its very best but still probably not the position to try out that new extend-an-orgasm technique. Standing positions tend to only work for quickies because his penis isn't the only thing that gets stiff.

Chances of getting caught: Choose a tree deep in the woods or in a park at night and you'll probably be fine. If either of you hear the tell-tale snapping of twigs (someone out walking the dog), it's not too difficult to untwine, adjust your clothes, and pretend you're just having a snog. OK, they might make a big swerve around you, sniff disapprovingly, or look embarrassed, but they're only jealous!

ON TOP OF A PICNIC TABLE

How you do it: Pack a picnic and head to the park when everyone else has gone home. Find a table in the picnic area, lay it, have a feast, then clear it off and lay each other… He stands in front, she lays back on the table and wraps her legs around his waist. It's ideal because she's facing one way, he's facing the other, so you can keep watch in both directions!

Why you'd risk it: I'm not a huge believer in all the supposed "hotspots" that continue to be "discovered" on the female body. On the other hand, anything that inspires you to try something new is fine by me! The picnic table position is supposedly fab for stimulating the A-spot (the Anterior Fornex Erogenous) because the angle of your vagina positions his penis for a direct hit. This hot spot was accidentally discovered in 1996 by scientists who were trying to find a cure for vaginal dryness. They were astonished to find 95 per cent of women became massively turned on when this area was stimulated. Many women had their first orgasm or found it led to more frequent and intense climaxes. The research methods that produced this evidence have since been questioned but no harm in mounting a little expedition anyway! The A-spot is purportedly halfway between the infamous G-spot and your cervix. Feel for a smooth area that's extremely sensitive to touch.

Chances of getting caught: High. Picnic tables tend to be found in reasonably public areas. And there would be absolutely no mistaking what you're up to if someone did happen to wander into view. Attempt under cover of darkness only.

ON A SWING

How you do it: If she's been a good (naughty) girl, she'll have thought to wear a long, loose skirt and no knickers. She lifts the skirt and sits forward on the seat. He stands in front, feet squarely placed on the floor, holds the sides of the seat firmly and draws her to him to penetrate. Then he swings her to and fro while he stands still.

Why you'd risk it: It's fun! You're bound to end up laughing because it's not easy doing it on a moving object. Chances are you won't achieve deep penetration because of the difficulty in coordination but that's not a bad thing. All of the nerve endings – or sensory perceptors – in the vagina are located within an inch or so of the vaginal entrance.

Chances of getting caught: You may get away with it in a playground late at night, but – and it's a BIG but – if you get caught and reported, you'll risk arrest for being way too adult in a children's zone. If the neighbours might be suspicious if you install a swing in the garden, consider buying a swing that you suspend indoors.

How to orgasm in five minutes flat

- **Use lube:** When time is short, using a lubricant is essential. There's no time for the vagina to lubricate naturally and sex will be painful without it. So, remember to go prepared!

- **Add a vibrator:** Holding a vibrator on the clitoral area is the quickest, most efficient way for a female to orgasm. If having sex outdoors, consider the extra noise factor!

- **Switch stimulation:** If something doesn't feel right within a minute, try something else. Change position and alternate between tongues and hands, and intercourse.

- **Do something new:** We quickly become desensitized to sexual sensations and experiences which is why the first time for anything, is often the best. New = erotic. Add something different to your repertoire: try a new location, time of the day, wear something sexy, tie each other up, watch a sexy film.

- **Do it yourself:** No-one is as expert at giving you an orgasm as you are yourself. If you're finding it hard to tip over the brink, finish yourself off and suggest your partner does the same. It doesn't mean you aren't good lovers, just that DIY gets a quicker result when time is short!

Outdoor sex... indoors

For those who don't dare do it alfresco

Some people are out the door with half their clothes ripped off the second you suggest having sex outside. Others aren't quite so adventurous. While you're revelling in the might-get-caught, rough-and-readiness of sex alfresco, they're peering worriedly over your shoulder, rather than gazing lustily at your breasts. Then there are the "Princess and the Pea" types – a pebble the size of a pinhead pricks their bottom or it's one degree below balmy and the whole thing's ruined. And yes, I am speaking from experience.

Hotels, swimming pools, in a **famous place** or **landmark...** change your location for some great new **indoor/outdoor** experiences.

"Let's do it right here, right now," I said to my new (sort-of) boyfriend, Richard. "What here?" he said, looking around him with disbelief, as though we were standing in the middle of a shopping centre during the January sales and I'd suggested a bit of rompy-pompy on top of the £5 bargain bin. We were, in fact, sitting at a picnic table near a river in pitch darkness at midnight, a good five minute walk from

Do it in different places

A quickie in bed, where you always have sex, doesn't quite have the exotic flavour you're after. It needs to be somewhere unorthodox, where you don't usually have sex. Remember, a quickie can be intercourse, oral, or hand stimulation.

- **In the kitchen:** She sits on the worktop, he stands in front of her. Even better if you have to push dirty dishes roughly out of the way to make room.
- **The bathroom:** Standing up in the shower, in the bath, or her standing with legs apart, hands on the sink for support, as he enters from behind.
- **The loo:** An odd choice, admittedly, but that's why it's a good choice! Pretend your parents have come for Sunday lunch and you've snuck in there while they're having a stroll around the garden. Add to the fantasy by leaving clothes on and simply unzipping and pulling knickers to one side.
- **The laundry:** Time it when the washing machine's on the spin cycle and it turns into a seat-size vibrator!
- **On the stairs:** Doing it on the stairs is ideal if height differences stop you from using certain positions. If one stands a few steps up and the other a few steps down, heights magically even out.
- **The garden shed:** A sneaky way to get the thrill of doing it outside, without actually being seen by your neighbours. Just be a tad careful where you put your hands, feet – and bottoms.

His top five hand-jobs

Use lubricant for all these techniques – a hand-job without it is like roast without the gravy. Don't finish his hand-job in company unless there's a good airflow. Semen has a strong, unmistakable smell and you'll be busted before you can say "God, how embarassing!"

1. The classic: This involves wrapping one or two fingers around the shaft of the penis and manipulating the foreskin, so it moves up and down with each stroke. You need to place your fingers exactly where he does at the starting position (ask him to show you how he masturbates). To vary this, make a ring with your forefinger and thumb and put it around the base of the penis. As you pull his penis upward, pull the ringed fingers downward to gently pull his testicles away from his body.

2. The favourite: This is a smooth, up-and-over technique that he will love! Hold your right hand in front of you, and turn it so the back of your hand is facing you with your thumb lifted up. Your elbow is cocked. Hold the base of his penis: the back of your hand and four fingers on the side of the penis facing you and your thumb on the side facing him. Slide slowly up the shaft in a firm, continuous movement and when you reach the part where the shaft meets the head, slightly twist your hand. Then, keeping your palm close to the head, pass your palm over the top of his penis and down the other side. Once you reach the base, slide it back over (in reverse) into the starting position. Repeat with your left hand and keep alternating.

3. Spanish style: Put some lubricant between your breasts, push them together to make a pretend vagina and let him thrust between them. Not only does it seem wickedly disrespectful (always a good thing in sex, I find!) to be aiming his lethal part straight at your face, he will faithfully follow you around Habitat every Sunday morning for a month if you let him ejaculate over you.

4. The twist: Imagine you're twisting the cap off a bottle of beer (if you really want to make his day, hand him one before you do this!) Grip the base of the penis with one hand, pulling the foreskin taut,

He will faithfully **follow you around Habitat** every Sunday morning for a month if you let him **ejaculate over you**.

and the head with the other. Now, twist the top hand firmly, return, then twist again, turning it into a continuous motion, slowing down or building up speed depending on his response. Your thumb should be on the frenulum (the stringy bit under the ridge where the head meets the shaft).

5. Finger lock: Clasp your hands and interlock your fingers, overlapping your thumbs, but leaving room for his penis to slip in the middle. Lower your hands over his penis, close your thumbs to take a firm hold, then slide your clasped hands up and down, twisting gently as you do.

Her top five hand-jobs

As with him, you'll get far better results if you add lubricant for all these techniques.

1. The classic: Place your palm over her pubic hair and bend your middle finger so it's angled ready to touch her clitoris, resting on the inner lips. Position your index and ring fingers so they're resting on the outer lips. Then use your middle finger to gently rub the clitoris up and down or in circles, maintaining a slow, steady rhythm.

Lots of women have a **"favourite" side**, to their clitoris, and you are more likely to discover it using the **"clock"** hand-job method.

Squeeze the other two fingers to push the outer lips together and provide extra pressure. A variation is to dip a finger inside her, then slowly slide it along the inner lips of the vagina, moving up toward the clitoris. Let your whole finger roll against the clitoris, then move back down to repeat. Don't touch the clitoris directly the first time.

2. Scissors: Put your index and middle finger together, hold them stiff, so they're resting on the inner lips, then move them rapidly from side to side, using a small, gentle movement. Next, "scissor" your fingers, kicking them in alternating directions. Again, keep the movement small or she'll hit the roof with pain, not pleasure.

3. The wall: Put two fingers inside her vagina, then curl them upward so you're pressing against the front wall (as though you're aiming for her stomach). Make sure they're butting up against (or even grab onto) her pubic bone. Massage this top area, using firm pressure, and you're stimulating the "inner clitoris" – the part which is hidden – and the über-sensitive front vaginal wall.

4. The clock: Imagine there's a clock dial surrounding the clitoris, then work your way around, spending five seconds in each "hour" position, making tiny circles with your fingertips. This ensures you don't overstimulate the clitoris, plus it gets you to concentrate on the edges of the clitoris, rather than the centre (which most women prefer). Lots of women have a "favourite" side and you're more likely to discover it this way. To make the feeling more intense, use your other hand to pull up the skin of the mons pubis (fleshy bit). This pulls the clitoris out from under its hood, exposing a larger area.

5. The roll: Use the clitoral hood (the fold of flesh protecting the clitoris) like you would a foreskin, moving it up and down rather than touching the clitoris. Using it as a buffer, roll it between your thumb and index finger to stimulate the clitoris. (You can use the same motion directly on the clitoris.)

3 Bet you haven't tried…

Time to get really naughty.

The world tends to divide into two types of couples: those who try anything and everything (S&M gear spilling out of their cupboards) and those who don't really try anything at all (a pair of naughty knickers stuffed amongst Bridget-Jones-style Big Pants). The majority of us fall into the latter category – through sheer laziness, fear (scared to suggest it, scared people like our parents will find out), or from romanticism (a perception that if you really love each other, you won't need any "false" stimulation – bollocks!).

To prevent the inevitable decline in desire that affects almost all long-term couples, I suggest you take a step towards the middle of these two extremes. Create a new category of couples who experiment with interesting things, but aren't reliant on them to enjoy great sex. If you tried out some earlier ideas and enjoyed the results, you're ready to push the boat out a little further into the erotic ocean. Again, don't panic! Despite the great risqué pictures in this feature, the ideas are adventurous but approached sensibly. I give you information about "risky" things you might be attracted to, then suggest a "wimp's way out": something naughty enough to "shock" your sexual system, but not so naughty it short-circuits the relationship.

SWINGING

Swingers are couples, usually in committed relationships, who like to have threesomes, foursomes, or moresomes with other couples. In the sex-mad 70s, this was easy to achieve: simply invite all your neighbours over, serve large martinis along with the fondue and cheese-and-pineapple-on-sticks, and you'd all be pooling the car keys before the first joint got stubbed out. In today's moral climate, putting a hand up the jumper of nice Mrs Bridgewater from next door, after your second glass of red, will probably end with handcuffs – but not quite the sort you were imagining.

Most **sex therapy** is aimed at making couples feel **comfortable sexually.** But new research suggests that **edginess, risk, and danger** are often needed to make **sex spectacular.**

Most swingers these days meet through personal ads or via the internet. Some couples keep it relatively private (well, as private as it can be), choosing only to play with one other couple at a time. Others attend swingers' parties or go to clubs, taking their pick from a broader selection.

Generally, all couples arrive as a couple, most participate as a couple and leave as a couple. "Closed" swinging is when one partner chooses not to be around while their lover is having sex with others (highly sensible, I'd have thought); "open" swinging means both participate, and "soft" swinging means you'll "heavy pet" with people

but draw the line at penetration. Not surprisingly, swinging comes with a hefty "try at your own risk" warning: you really do need to be a special" type of person to cope with it. Most end up feeling jealous and in lots of cases, motivation is lop-sided. One partner wants to try something, the other goes along with it for fear of losing them if they don't. It can and does lead to split-ups, albeit interesting ones. I've interviewed at least four couples who have swapped with another couple – and stayed.

> If you **chicken out** and head to the bar, it doesn't mean you've failed. You have succeeded in **pushing yourself out of your comfort zone**.

Wimp's way out:

Get the thrill of swinging without the down side by going to a swingers' club and watching but not participating. Choosing a club, planning what to wear, imagining all sorts of scenarios, finally turning up, giggly but excited – the anticipation of doing something terribly daring will already have injected more excitement into your relationship than you've seen since the new IKEA opened down the road. And you haven't even ventured inside yet!

Once you do, you'll find clubs are usually quite dark and anonymous and it's relatively easy to hang back and observe without being asked to participate. Most have websites, so don't be scared to email or call first to ask what "rules" there are (most clubs are cool with you just watching but some aren't). Lots ask you to join as a member but it's a legal formality – you can sign in as Elvis and Priscilla from Graceland for all they care. Bring lots of cash for the entrance fee and drinks, and aim to get there about two hours after it opens so there's plenty going on. Once inside, walk around and explore. There are usually several rooms and a general area that has porn playing. "Private rooms" are where couples can go to have sex. Sometimes there's a dance floor. Expect a lot of eyeing up and flirting, public

---

If you keep doing what you've always done, **you'll keep getting what you've always got**. If your love life rates as "content", **take a risk**.

---

snogging (and more), and a general air of seediness (which is, of course, why you're there). Stay as long as you're having fun, leave if you feel uncomfortable; don't drink too much.

WOMEN WITH WOMEN

It's not just men who harbour secret fantasies of big-breasted blondes mud-wrestling – plenty of women are bi-curious. Wanting to experiment with the same sex isn't a problem if you're single and up for trying new things but for long-term couples who've pledged monogamy, it poses a dilemma. You've promised not to sleep with anyone else – but do the rules apply if it's someone of your own sex?

Plenty of men respond to her initial suggestions of same-sex experimentation with delighted enthusiasm, rather like they've just won the sexual lottery. But that's usually because (1) he assumes he

will be allowed to watch and (2) he has a fixed script in his head of what will happen (the girls will kiss, fondle, and lick each other, putting on a fine show for him, but ultimately be bored with female flesh and beg him to join in and "properly" satisfy them). In reality, this often isn't the case. If she does allow him to watch, the guy is often excluded as the girls get down to it and he can't see as much

Remember, just because it **turns you on**, doesn't mean it's going to work for your partner: one person's **wet dream** is another's **wet blanket**.

as he thought. Then there's the risk that once she's batted for the home team, she'll want to stay. Some men "permit" their partner to experiment with women, others simply see it as sex with another person, which contravenes the relationship rules.

Wimp's way out:

A safe way to indulge a same-sex fantasy is to visit a strip or lap dancing club and let her flirt with the strippers and/or get a lap dance. No longer just frequented by sad old drunks, some clubs now boast a clientele of smart, young couples. To make sure she gets the attention, load her up with the cash – the person doing the tipping gets all the attention. Some clubs have private peep booths or VIP rooms where dancers masturbate or perform erotic acts (you pay by the minute). Ask if they have "couples' specials" where, in private, dancers perform to both or just one of you.

Voyeurism

A voyeur likes to watch other people have sex but doesn't want to join in (most are happy to masturbate). In a sense we're all voyeurs: few of us would be able to resist watching people have sex if we knew we wouldn't get caught. True "peeping Toms" actively search for spying opportunities (e.g. curtains not drawn) and are often unable to become aroused without "spying". Others pay sex workers to perform, or indulge in what's called "dogging". Under the guise of taking the dog for a walk, they head to known areas where exhibitionistic couples have sex in their car or singles masturbate.

Be clear about what you want: **Is this a one-time experience** or do you want it to be a **regular part of your sex life?**

Wimp's way out:
Peep booths perform the same purpose, without the risk of you being arrested (or shocking poor old Rover into an early doggie grave). Head towards the red light district in any city and you'll find them inside strip clubs and lots of adult book stores. Typically you go inside, sit on a stool, put money or tokens into the meter and a screen lifts or glass defogs to reveal a sex worker putting on a show behind glass. Sometimes you can request specific acts (for extra cash of course).

Thrills without spills

I was (a naïve) nineteen the first time someone asked me to do something "kinky". My fiancé (the first of three, before I actually followed through) tentatively suggested we turn to the porn channel while abroad and watch a "sexy movie" together.

Shocked, horrified, offended (and any other negative emotion you can think of), I drew myself up to full height (an impressive five foot five, to his six feet four) and said, outraged, "Absolutely not!" "No

---

Talk it through. Ask your partner why it appeals. Let them **reassure you** it doesn't mean you don't turn them on, you simply **want variety**.

---

problem", he said, continuing to unpack, unconcerned. But I kept thinking about it. And thinking. And on the third day I said, "OK, let's give it a whirl", and, sexually, we never looked back. (OK, I looked forward obviously, but never back.)

My reaction is typical of most people. Feeling threatened and/or slightly shocked, we turn so moral and righteous, we'd make an 80-year-old nun look liberal. Persuading your partner to try new things sounds so simple… except it's often not. Turn the page for some ideas on how to cope and what to do, on either side of the fence.

Sexploration: the rules

- **Talk through** exactly what will happen, being as specific as possible, so there are no surprises. If your partner won't be persuaded, accept defeat graciously and suggest an alternative.

- **Respect that not everyone** has the same desires. Listen to what your partner wants to try too.

- **Try something reasonable.** If it won't harm you, try not to say no just because you think you won't like it. How do you know if you've never tried it?

- **Set rules** and stick to them: how far are each of you prepared to go and under what circumstances?

- **Decide on a "safe word"** that means "Stop now". Make it something you're definitely not going to say accidentally.

- **Remember your relationship** is more important, at every moment, than the experience you're having. Constantly check in with each other.

- **Don't be afraid** to use your "safe word" to stop the experience if you feel upset. It doesn't mean you're prudish, just prudent.

- **If your partner gets upset,** stop everything immediately and go to their emotional rescue.

YOU want to try something new, they don't...

- **Remember, just because it turns you on, doesn't mean it's going to make your partner shudder with delight:** One person's passion is another's passion-killer.
- **Be positive and confident when asking for what you want:** If you make a big deal about asking or look terrified once it's out of your mouth, they'll also think it's a big deal. Say it confidently and casually and they're far more likely to agree. This is only possible if you truly believe it's harmless fun. If you're secretly worried it's dodgy, slay your own personal demons first by finding out more about it.
- **Be clear about what you want:** Do you want to try it for fun, or make it a regular part of your sex life? Most people can cope with doing "kinky" things once or twice, but few want to do it every single session.
- **Talk it through:** Asking someone to try something new can make them feel insecure. They think: "Why am I not enough any more?" Talk about the reasons why it appeals to you, tactfully. Reassuring them they're very sexy, often fixes the problem.
- **Don't spring any surprises!:** Tying her up and saying, "Aha! Now I've got you!" and bringing in the call girl isn't wise if you want to make it to that next wedding anniversary!

THEY want to try something new, you don't...

4 Great sex games

Because grown-ups need fun too!

Some people love games, others loathe them. But even if you are the type who develops chronic diarrhoea at the mere mention of the word "charades", you might just find something to tickle your fancy here. As I always say (over and over until you're sick of hearing it): the couple who play together, stay together. The reason I keep repeating myself is this: *it's true*!! Stop playing and you'll fall out of love. Keep having fun and you'll stay together. Simple as that. Now, do as you're told. I order you to have fun!

TO HAVE A BIT OF A LAUGH

- **Make obscene phone calls:** One of you goes outside or to another room, then dials the other, pretending they have no idea who they've just called – but have every intention of being shockingly rude. Ask questions like: "What are you wearing?". Give instructions like: "Pull your panties to one side for me", "Reach down and grab that big, lovely erection you've got". At first, the person you've called is shocked and outraged, but then they seem oddly turned on by it all…

- **Be flashers:** Turn the lights off, then take it in turns to light one area of your own body with a torch. Each lit body part must be touched, stroked and/or licked for two minutes, then the torch gets passed onto the next person. (Note to boys: It gets very, very boring if the only thing ever under the spotlight is long and cylindrical.)

- **Play "dress up":** PVC nurses outfits, baby doll lingerie, all-in-one catsuits – they're straight out of the 80s and tons of fun. You pay through the nose for them in a sex shop and they're not terribly well made, but if you like the look of them, why not! If the

Stop playing and you'll fall out of love. Keep having fun and you'll stay together. Simple as that.
Having fun isn't a luxury; its essential.

thought of you dressed up as Nurse Betty/Spiderman, makes you want to scream with hilarity rather than lust, think tasteful. For her, a little kimono with nothing underneath, high heels, and no knickers. For him, a bare chest with a pair of great jeans, top button undone.

- **Fantasy dice:** Write down and number the beginning of six fantasies (something like "And there I was – in the middle of an orgy"), then take turns throwing the dice. When the person lands on a number, they have to complete the corresponding fantasy out loud. It's a sneaky, not-too-embarrassing way to find out your partner's secret turn-ons because we rarely make up a fantasy that doesn't appeal to us.

- **Be a sex therapist:** One of you goes somewhere private to take a call from a "patient" you're trying to help. The patient rings and pretends to ask for advice on how to please their partner. If you like this one, get the therapist to arrange an appointment to give "hands-on" demonstrations of each technique.

Make your own **sex coupons** and leave promised treats for your partner to discover. **Their reward for being very good is you being very bad.**

- **Look, no hands!** If you're too dependent on your hands to turn each other on, tie your partner's hands together then ask them to seduce you. They've got no option but to up the oral quotient by using their lips, teeth, and tongue – or parts of themselves they wouldn't usually dream of using. If you really want to make things interesting, tie *both* of your hands behind your backs.

- **Play cards:** *supersexdeck* is my card game, which includes cards that have an intercourse position on the front and info on the back. Pick a card, any card. They are designed to help long-term lovers be more sexually adventurous and new lovers find each other's sexual triggers. If you're shy, they're a godsend. Let the cards speak for you.

- **Play with food:** Smear it, insert it, drip it on and lick it off – food is such a versatile sex toy, the possibilities are endless. Don't spray anything into the vagina or anus because its dangerous. But otherwise, have some fun!

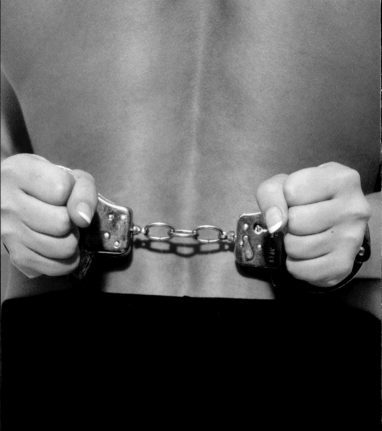

SEX TOYS

Walking into a sex shop can be bewildering, so I've compiled a list of items you're likely to be drawn to. You can use this to shop online if you're shy, but I'd highly recommend you visit a reputable sex shop together first so that you can pick the products up, feel, and test them. It's also a naughty, sexy thing to do!

- **Vibrators:** Every woman's best friend, vibrators come in all shapes and sizes, from a buzzing lipstick to a throbbing 10-inch fleshlike (terrifying) thing. Narrow the selection by deciding what you want from yours: if it's for masturbation and you're into penetration with clitoral stimulation, go for a "rabbit". "Wand" vibrators – small vibrators that you hold against the clitoris – are ideal for use during intercourse. Test how quiet it is and if you can vary the speed.

- **Dildos:** These are imitation penises of varying sizes. Unlike vibrators, they don't vibrate. If you like the feeling of fullness, they're good to insert during oral sex.

- **Vibrating penis rings:** These are penis rings – usually rubber – with little vibrators attached for clitoral stimulation. To use them effectively, he should use a grinding circular motion to keep the vibrator in contact with the clitoris as much as possible. They're cute, fun – and surprisingly effective!

- **S&M gear:** Those menacing looking studded collars, leather outfits and masks are sometimes enough to send you scuttling out the shop door. But others are intrigued rather than intimidated. My advice is, don't invest too much at the start – and make sure both agree!

Her top five oral sex techniques

1. The classic: Separate the vaginal lips with your fingers, find the clitoris and lick around the edges, slowly and gently. Then relax your tongue and wiggle it side-to-side and up and down over the clitoris and/or clitoral hood (depending on how sensitive she is). On orgasm, press your flat tongue against the clitoral head, continuing to lick, or simply let her push against you. Don't remove your tongue until she says so – women's orgasms last much longer than yours!

> Don't **remove your tongue** until **she says so** – women's orgasms **last much longer than yours!**

2. The ice-cream: Make your tongue flat and wide, like you're licking an ice-cream, and start with long, slow, wet licks on the inner lips. Move from this into a swishing motion – imagine you're catching the drips off an ice-cream. As your tongue swishes randomly, you're now teasing the edges of the clitoris. Next, alternate long, flat, ice-cream licks on or around the clitoris with firm, short, fast licks using a tensed tongue. (If the clitoris shrinks or she pulls away, you're being too rough.) Alternate the techniques, then settle on the one she seems to like the best, continuing it through to orgasm.

3. The zig-zag: This technique stops you over-stimulating one area and making the clitoris over-sensitive. The zig-zag involves alternating vertical strokes of the tongue on the bottom of the clitoris, with horizontal strokes across the whole of it. Horizontal strokes are usually more pleasurable, so do about seven of those to one vertical. Once she's highly aroused, add in some diagonal licks. Tilt your head to the side (your ear near or on her thigh) and using the side of your tongue, start from a low corner point and finish by brushing up against the clitoral head.

4. Hands on: Let your finger follow behind your tongue so she has a contrast of sensation (soft tongue, firm fingers) or put a finger in her mouth. She'll either give it "mini" fellatio or suck it the way she wants you to lick her. Insert a finger inside her vagina and thrust it in and out; reach up and use both hands to play with her breasts. If she likes anal stimulation, try simultaneously putting your thumb inside her anus, a finger into her vagina and your mouth on her clitoris.

5. Mirror, mirror: Lots of women think their vagina is a weird, purpley, squishy thing. So a guy who looks at it with lust and/or wonder scores big points. In the early- and mid-stages or oral sex, suddenly pull back, stopping to stare at her genitals, letting your eyes also gaze over the rest of her (gorgeous) body. Only pause for a few moments so she gets the message, and for God's sake don't do it as she's about to climax!

His top five oral sex techniques

1. Lollipop: This one is often used in porn films because it allows him to see exactly what's going on. To fuel this fantasy, drop to your knees. (Depending on your heights, he might need to stand on something – you need good access to his testicles.) Lift his penis to expose his testicles, then find the line which runs between them (it's a tiny ridge that's often a darker colour). Find where this starts on the underside of his testicles, and that's where your lollipop lick starts – continuing, very slowly to the tip of his penis. Repeat the full-length licks (at least 10), then move into the "classic".

2. The classic: Use one hand to hold the base of the penis and let saliva pool in your mouth (your tongue needs to keep him nice and slippery.) Make a loose fist with your other hand and slide it up and down his penis, closing it when you reach the head. Get the hand motion right first, then add your mouth, letting your hand act as an extension of it. Create a snug vacuum (but don't suck), then slide up and down, your hand following your mouth. If you're not very coordinated, hold your hand still and move your mouth up and down.

3. The twist and swirl: Add oomph to the "classic" or any oral technique by adding the "twist and swirl". The combination of firm fingers and a soft tongue feels great and it's easy to master. As you're using your hand to masturbate him, twist it slightly once it reaches the head and at the same time, swirl the flat of your tongue around the rim of the head. A simple but oh-so-effective move! Also try frenulum flicks: flicking it using a tensed tongue; or make like a butterfly and "flutter" the frenulum.

4. Ball games: The greatest compliment you can give him is looking like you want to be down there – and one of the best ways to show this is to explore all of him. Take one or both testicles in

Often used in **porn films** because it allows him to see **exactly what's going on**. To fuel this fantasy, **drop to your knees**.

your mouth, hum lightly, suck gently and/or swirl your tongue around. (If you don't want to swallow, switching to testicle stimulation while working on him with your hand is a good alternative.)

5. Rimming: Rimming is oral anal stimulation (sometimes called analingus). It involves licking, flicking, or inserting a stiff tongue into the anal passage and thrusting like a pretend penis. It feels great (for both sexes actually) because the area is highly sensitive and loaded with nerve endings. If you're worried about germs, STI's, or generally squeamish, put a barrier between it and you – try a piece of clingfilm or cut open a condom and lay it across the opening.

5 Cosmic connection

How to put the *Ahhh!* Into Om…

I have to say, I initially approached the topic of spiritual sex with great scepticism. They might well be concepts and principles drawn from musty, ancient texts (which makes us automatically assume the content is wise), but let's all be honest here: some of it really is a load of bollocks. Like, does anyone really "get down on all fours and pretend to be lions roaring at one another"? Please, God, tell me no. I can think of some very good reasons to get down on all fours but pretending to be a lion isn't one of them.

I'm also not terribly impressed by claims that loss of semen weakens a man and shortens his life. If this is true, how come Hugh Hefner is still alive then? A spiritual sex fan, I wasn't! Until I started reading in earnest and… if you can get past the "let's-all-pretend-we're-little-flowers-growing-in-the-earth" stuff, there's actually some damn good, sound advice mixed in there.

I emerged from the research pleasantly surprised – and, dare I say, a tad converted! (Academic research, not practical, by the way – sadly, I really don't lie around instantly testing out every theory with a never-ending stream of gorgeous men!)

Now, before I attempt to pass on what I think are the best bits, I must point out I'm not even going to attempt to summarize the true spiritual meanings and intellectual theories behind my discoveries. Fascinating as it is, the sex part of the *Kama Sutra* is, in fact, just one book in a series of seven, and to truly embrace and understand Tantra takes a lifetime. Our lifestyles, beliefs, and values have changed, so some of the cultural and spiritual beliefs could be hard to relate to. Instead, I'm going to focus on practical sex tips or lessons we can learn. If you like what you're reading and think you'd like to explore more, put down that bowl of lentils and get onto the net or into a bookstore to buy a book on spiritual sex. (You could try my *Kama Sutra*!)

Does anyone really **"get down on all fours and pretend to be lions roaring at one another"**? Please, God, tell me no.

TANTRA

What is it?: It's an eastern science that emerged out of a rebellion against current Hindu beliefs that suggested sex was a no-no if you wanted "spiritual enlightenment". It's been around since the seventh century and honours the sacred union of the male and female energies that create life. Shiva (male), is the embodiment of pure consciousness and Shakti (female), pure energy.

The basic principles: Sex is slowed down. There's gradual, controlled thrusting, rather than the usual frenetic free-for-all. This enables women to use learnt techniques like vaginal tensing and

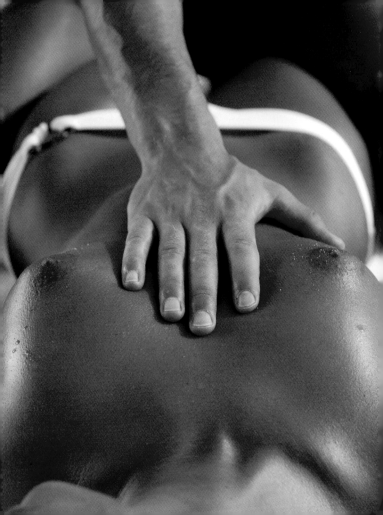

flexing – a posh version of pelvic floor exercises. It's not a myth that tantric sex can go on for one or two hours, by the way, but the jury's still out on whether longer sex sessions lead to more enjoyable sex. Tantra also teaches you how to stay in the moment. If you're the type to drift off while your partner's still gamely thrusting away ("How will I fit in the gym tomorrow?"), the "connecting" exercises could be useful. Traditional sex therapy encourages people to lose themselves in the experience, Tantra is all about staying fully aware and present.

> It's not a myth that **tantric sex** can go on for **hours,** but the jury's still out on whether **longer sex** equals more **enjoyable sex**.

Breathing exercises are designed to improve sexual tone, prolong intercourse, and can help men with premature ejaculation.

Lessons to learn:
- It encourages couples to stop being time- or orgasm-focused.
- It involves the heart as well as other parts.
- There's no place in Tantra for lovers to be selfish – it's all about giving to each other.

Not so sure:
- Men are encouraged to prolong love-making (the old "retain your semen" thing again), which buys into the myth that women climax through penetration.
- Rituals are important. Some people love this aspect, others hate having to go through long, complicated processes.

- Tantra often refers to mixing of body fluids ("nectar" or "love juices"). If you're not having monogamous sex, mixing is about as sensible as lying in the middle of a road during rush hour. Safe sex and condoms aren't figured in.

KAMA SUTRA

What is it?: It's an ancient sex manual written between the third and fifth centuries. There are actually seven books in total, though only the second is devoted purely to sex. (Worth wading through the others, however, if you'd like to know how to break into a harem or how to conduct an affair successfully!) The *Kama Sutra* is much, much more than just acrobatic positions for intercourse, though most modern interpretations tend to focus almost exclusively on this.

The basic principles: Interestingly, all the complex seduction and sexual techniques actually aren't aimed at couples in love. If you love each other, all you need to do is "let yourself go and be led by instinct". (Oh really?) The techniques are designed to help you achieve this state. Some positions seem yoga-like because they're designed to facilitate meditation as a couple. They're also intended to allow you to have sex for one or two hours with minimal movement needed. During this time, you will exchange vital energies – or fall asleep. (My money's on the latter.)

Lessons to learn:

- It recognised female orgasm in a time when others thought there was no such thing.
- It recommends the man ensures she climaxes before he does.
- Sexual boredom and monotony are seen as the reason why couples split.

- It's common in India for men to be encouraged to read the *Kama Sutra* before marrying. (If the West had encouraged sex research, I think affairs and divorce rates would fall dramatically!)

Not so sure:

- A man and woman live as one single body and soul. Independent types and commitment-phobes would run screaming for the hills.
- Those one- to two- hour sessions… who's got time?
- Some of the positions require rubber limbs and plasticine penises.

TAOISM

What is it?: It's a book written in the sixth century that talks about the yin (female) and the yang (male) and the flow of energy between them. This is called ch'i and it's the same life force which flows in the human body. Harmony is achieved by teaching people how to live within the flux of changing energy.

The basic principles: Taoism recognized that men can have multiple orgasms because orgasm and ejaculation are two separate processes. This is because ejaculation is simply the series of contractions which pump the semen out; the feeling of orgasm happens in the brain. It teaches men to orgasm without ejaculation through long, involved "Sting-like" processes which train the brain and body to separate the two. There's a focus on lots of foreplay and nine types of thrusting to try – the aim being to achieve 81 thrusts (one set of nine of each type)!

Lessons to learn:

- It recognizes that male desire is easier to ignite and quick to burn out, while females take longer but tend to last longer.
- There's an emphasis on slow, prolonged foreplay with lots of finger and mouth action for her.

Not so sure:

- Who's going to keep count until you get to 81?
- Ejaculation is permitted only when necessary. Call my male friends old-fashioned, but none thought this was a good thing.
- Separating orgasm from ejaculation is something I've read lots about, but I've never met a man who's actually mastered it. Most women aren't that fussed and would probably be highly suspicious, rather than in raptures, of an apparent orgasm without any evidence (men fake it too).
- One suggested method for stopping orgasm is for him to "gnash his teeth". This, I suspect, would not be terribly sexy for her.

Other reasons why you might like it: (Told you I was being won over!)

- Intimacy – high on the spiritual agenda – is something lots of women and some men crave. New research suggests it may be the magic ingredient for good, lifelong sex.
- Lots of the soppy stuff (hands on hearts, breathing in time with each other) can make people feel safe and more secure.
- It's creative and new – both score huge points!
- Couples are encouraged to live in the moment, take time out, and watch stress levels.
- You're taught to let go of body judgements. "Fat days" don't exist because you learn to love all of you.
- There's an emphasis on self-exploration, learning about your body and how it works. The more you know, the better lovers you are.
- There's no rush to orgasm and it's not orgasm-focused.
- You're told to make your bedroom a sacred space. Clean sheets and scented candles could make a nice change from dog-hair, coffee-cup stains, and toast crusts.

Toy with Tao and Tantra
Advanced stuff to try

Fancy a dabble into some more advanced spiritual stuff? Try any of the following:

TO HAVE A FULL-BODY ORGASM
Forget clitoral-, vaginal-, G-spot-, or multiple orgasms, the full-body orgasm supposedly makes all the competition pale in comparison… well, according to those into Tantra. They claim by learning certain

The famous Kinsey report found that at least **15 per cent** of both **men** and **women** are capable of **multiple orgasms** – you could be one!

Tantric techniques, you can flood your entire body with orgasmic sensations, and you can stay there for minutes or over an hour. You accomplish this by opening your "chakras" – the body's energy centres. There's one located at the base of your spine, stomach, genitals, throat, forehead, and top of your head.

• **Start with massage:** Her massage concentrates on the lower back, spine, and the inside surface of her arms and legs.

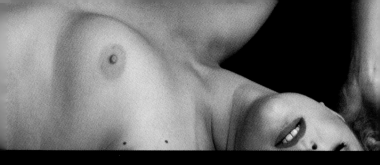

His focuses on the central area of the feet, which stimulates the liver (which controls and releases blood needed for erection).

- **Get the balance right:** Taoists encourage men to absorb the woman's fluids. It's called "the great liberation of the three peaks". In non-Tao terms, this means he must lick her lips and tongue, her breasts and her genitals. Secretions from these parts are supposedly fabulous for his health – chances are she won't argue otherwise.
- **Read the signs:** Spiritualists believe it's possible for both of you to achieve "supreme pleasure" if the man pays attention to five, significant signs of female desire. (In case you hadn't noticed, a lot of spiritual sex is focused on the female which could possibly explain my warming enthusiasm!). This is what you're looking for: (1) When she blushes and her body temperature rises, she's in the mood for "tender play". (2) When her nipples harden and small drops of sweat appear around her nose, she's ready to be penetrated. (3) If her throat or lips seem dry, she wants faster and deeper thrusts. (4) When her lubrication turns "slippery", he should move into the "deep explosion" (keep thrusting and don't bloody stop) and squeeze his bod against hers, each time with "more insistence". (5) When he spots secretion of a thick fluid on her thighs, she's reached the "high tide" of orgasmic explosion.

Sadly for him, he's forced to stay paddling in the shallow end. Instead of being able to let go and orgasm after all that hard work, he's advised to immediately begin his breathing exercises to postpone ejaculation for as long as possible.

The two of you then switch into various intercourse positions, in search of the infamous "supreme pleasure". The whole thing sounds (and is) both pleasurable and a pain in the ass. Speaking of bottoms, by the way, there's more than the odd technique involving anal penetration for him in spiritual sex, the rectum being the home of the male "G-spot" (prostate gland).

TO DELAY EJACULATION
- **Find the "MillionDollar Point":** All three spiritual schools of thought – Tao, Tantra, and *Kama Sutra* – have umpteen techniques to stave the inevitable spilling of "sacred seed". One of the oldest Tao techniques involves pressing the "Million Dollar Point" while he contracts his PC muscle (the one you use to stop yourself from urinating). This helps delay ejaculation by interrupting the ejaculatory reflex. This isn't an easy technique and is best mastered by the man initially, then taught to her.

Ideally guys, you'd push your finger inside your anus, up to the first joint, searching for a small indentation. The squeamish could try to find it by pressing it externally through the perineum (between the testicles and anus).

Spritual sex can be ideal for **older men**. As the saying goes; **"What young men want to do all night, takes older men all night to do"**.

- **Do a Finger Lock:** When you're hovering dangerously close to a spill-the-seed moment, press the three middle fingers of your strongest hand into the Million Dollar Point, hard enough to stop the flow of semen. (Do it externally, pushing on the perineum.) You're basically pushing your middle finger against the urethral tube which swells when close to ejaculation, making it easier to find. The other fingers press on each side of the tube to hold it in place. Once you've done this, contract your PC muscle and draw your orgasmic energy up to your brain. You will, understandably, lose your erection, but that's sort of the point, and it will return with a vengeance!

A taster of other cosmic stuff...

- **Mantras** are spoken or chanted during Tantric sex, the most famous being *"om mani padme hum"*. *"Mani"* means thunderbolt (referring to his penis), *"padme"* means lotus (vagina), and *"hum"* is the highest form of enlightenment. Tantrikas chant to awaken sexual energy and to mimic the energy vibration of the universe.

- **The five M's or "pancamakara"** appears, on the surface, to be hedonistic heaven – a feast followed by an orgy (now we're talking!). The first four M's involve eating and drinking food and wine with supposed aphrodisiac qualities. The fifth M is *"maithuna"*; ritualistic sex which allows you to experience *"higher"* pleasure while your body's still digesting the physical type. People moved very little during these sexual acts. Versions of this are taught today by Tantric gurus who explain the complex procedures required to transfer sexual energy between you.

- **For those who like to keep things simple...** For harmonious sex press similar body parts together – lips to lips, hands to hands, genitals to genitals. For excitement and stimulation, press dissimiliar body parts – mouth to genitals, mouth to breast, penis to anus, etc.

The 10 all-time best show-off sex positions

LEGGING IT

Inspired by the *Kama Sutra*, this position ensures the vagina is fully open to allow for maximum penetration. She is fully exposed, showing her "wet and longing" parts to her partner, which can be one hell of a turn-on for both of you. He has a great view, watching his penis move in and out. You can't kiss which ups the erotic tension.

BALANCED BABE

He sits on a chair; she straddles him, then moves one leg at a time to rest her ankles on his shoulders. If he's a fan of look-but-can't-do-anything-about-it lap-dancing, this will make his year. He cops a full view of her bits and she squeezes her thighs together to increase pressure on his penis. Excellent for a man who needs extra friction to stimulate him to climax (older or a few too many drinks). Because both are precariously balanced, he's not able to stimulate her clitoris, so oral sex or hand stimulation before or after is a good idea.

SIDE STRADDLE

A pose with significance, the shape of this pose replicates a specific pattern the ancient Chinese used when fusing two pieces of Jade together. She lies on her side, bending one leg at the knee and drawing it upwards. He kneels behind her, straddling her side on and entering her at a sideways angle, holding her shoulder to keep her in place. It's precise positioning, which gets you both in the mood for controlled, disciplined sex.

THE BULL

Tantra doesn't shy from animalistic sex and acting out the postures of animals is seen as "liberating" for both sexes. This typical rear-entry position means she "surrenders" to him completely… but she can lean backwards or forwards to alter the angle of the vagina, so is still (semi) in control. It allows both to fantasize and he can thrust deeply, with a fabulous view of her buttocks thrown in for good measure!

CARNAL CLASSIC

Tantra specializes in postures designed to create equilibrium in body, mind, and spirit. This position – the woman entwined, completely supported by the man – appears frequently in erotic Hindu art. An almost identical position features in the *Kama Sutra*'s repertoire, this time designed to encourage passion and creativity. Not for the faint-hearted, this can be made easier if she leans against a wall and pushes her back into it for leverage. A favourite show-off position, it's primal and perfect for a quickie.

PASSION PICK UP

Despite popular perception, the *Kama Sutra* only describes about
23 positions, with lots involving the woman lying on her back with
her legs in a variety of positions. But even subtle changes in position can
make an enormous difference to the angle of penetration. A variation on
"Legging It" (see page 86), the man kneels instead of sits, pulling her high,
and aiming for front-wall stimulation. G-spot fans will love it, but it's also
ideal if he wants to work on her clitoris.

TOPSY TURVY

Who said the missionary position is boring! Spin it around for a sensational twist. If he's adventurous, he'll enter in the traditional position (heads the same end) and slowly spin till he's facing the opposite way. The more sensible penetrate while in position (and yes, it is difficult). She'll like it because her clitoris and labia are in contact with his pelvis, adding much needed pressure. If he's into anal stimulation, she's in the perfect place to penetrate with a well-lubricated finger. If she's into toe-sucking, this is the position for you!

THE TANTRIC MELT

A version of a Tantric sitting posture, this ensures you'll "be as one" by "dissolving" into each other. Eye contact combined with close torsos makes it intimate and you can practise synchronizing your breath (if it appeals!). Interestingly, this pose puts both of you in a power position. She's on top, so can control the rhythm, speed, and depth of thrusting, but she's also effectively sitting in his lap, which is a traditionally submissive female pose. If she sat higher and rested her thighs in the crook of his elbow, he could lift her, taking complete control.

TOTALLY BONKERS

Advanced isn't the word for this position; bonkers probably is. If you're using a chair, make sure it's wedged firmly up against a wall. (A very hard bed can also work.) She leans her shoulders back against his chest as he penetrates, tipping her bottom upward toward him to make penetration possible. If he keeps slipping out (and he will), she spreads her legs wider and tips her bottom up even higher. It is possible. Just.

49

THE CAVE

The *Kama Sutra* rather charmingly extols the virtues of positions like this because she offers her "red cave" for him to admire before penetration. Not for girls who find touching their toes a challenge; supple, s-t-r-e-t-c-h-y limbs are a necessity. Usual thrusting is impossible, instead rock in a "see-saw" motion. With legs closed, the vaginal canal becomes invitingly narrow; she spreads her legs for wider access and deeper penetration.

10

Index

Acknowledgements

All photography by John Davis.
DK would like to thank Laurence Errington for the index.